每人都有份！

【美】谢拉·布鲁斯◎著

【美】佩姬·比林-弗莱◎绘

范晓星◎译

U0266045

天津出版传媒集团

新蕾出版社

图书在版编目（CIP）数据

每人都有份！/（美）布鲁斯（Bruce,S.）著；
（美）比林–弗莱（Billin-Frye,P.B.）绘；范晓星译.—
天津：新蕾出版社，2015.1（2024.12重印）
（数学帮帮忙·互动版）
书名原文：Everybody Wins!
ISBN 978-7-5307-6194-6

Ⅰ.①每… Ⅱ.①布…②比…③范… Ⅲ.①数学–
儿童读物 Ⅳ.①O1–49

中国版本图书馆 CIP 数据核字(2014)第 272522 号

Everybody Wins!　by Sheila Bruce;
Illustrated by Paige Billin-Frye.
Copyright ⓒ2001 by Kane Press, Inc.
All rights reserved, including the right of reproduction in whole or in part in any
form. This edition published by arrangement with Kane Press, Inc. New York, NY,
represented by Lerner Publishing Group through The ChoiceMaker Korea Co.
agency.
Simplified Chinese translation copyright ⓒ 2013 by New Buds Publishing House
(Tianjin) Limited Company
ALL RIGHTS RESERVED
本书中文简体版专有出版权经由中华版权代理中心授予新蕾出版社（天津）有
限公司。未经许可，不得以任何方式复制或抄袭本书的任何部分。
津图登字：02-2012-221

出版发行：天津出版传媒集团
　　　　　　新蕾出版社
http://www.newbuds.com.cn
地　　址：天津市和平区西康路 35 号(300051)
出 版 人：马玉秀
电　　话：总编办 (022)23332422
　　　　　发行部 (022)23332679　23332351
传　　真：(022)23332422
经　　销：全国新华书店
印　　刷：天津新华印务有限公司
开　　本：787mm×1092mm　1/16
印　　张：3
版　　次：2015 年 1 月第 1 版　2024 年 12 月第 26 次印刷
定　　价：12.00 元

著作权所有，请勿擅用本书制作各类出版物，违者必究。
如发现印、装质量问题，影响阅读，请与本社发行部联系调换。
地址：天津市和平区西康路 35 号
电话:(022)23332351　邮编:300051

无处不在的数学

资深编辑　卢　江

　　人们常说"兴趣是最好的老师",有了兴趣,学习就会变得轻松愉快。数学对于孩子来说或许有些难,因为比起语文,数学显得枯燥、抽象,不容易理解,孩子往往不那么喜欢。可许多家长都知道,学数学对于孩子的成长和今后的生活有多么重要。不仅数学知识很有用,学习数学过程中获得的数学思想和方法更会影响孩子的一生,因为数学素养是构成人基本素质的一个重要因素。但是,怎样才能让孩子对数学产生兴趣呢?怎样才能激发他们兴致勃勃地去探索数学问题呢?我认为,让孩子读些有趣的书或许是不错的选择。读了这套"数学帮帮忙",我立刻产生了想把它们推荐给教师和家长朋友们的愿望,因为这真是一套会让孩子爱上数学的好书!

　　这套有趣的图书从美国引进,原出版者是美国资深教育专家。每本书讲述一个孩子们生活中的故事,由故事中出现的问题自然地引入一个数学知识,然后通过运用数学知识解决问题。比如,从帮助外婆整理散落的纽扣引出分类,从为小狗记录藏骨头的地点引出空间方位等等。故事素材全部来源于孩子们的真实生活，不是童话，不是幻想，而是鲜活的生活实例。正是这些发生在孩子身边的故事，让孩子们懂得，数学无处不在并且非常有用；这些鲜活的实例也使得抽象的概念更易于理解，更容易激发孩子学习数学的兴趣，让他们逐渐爱上数学。这样的教育思想和方法与我国近年来提倡的数学教育理念是十分吻合的！

这是一套适合5~8岁孩子阅读的书，书中的有趣情节和生动的插画可以将抽象的数学问题直观化、形象化，为孩子的思维活动提供具体形象的支持。如果亲子共读的话，家长可以带领孩子推测情节的发展，探讨解决难题的办法，让孩子在愉悦的氛围中学到知识和方法。

值得教师和家长朋友们注意的是，在每本书的后面，出版者还加入了"互动课堂"及"互动练习"，一方面通过一些精心设计的活动让孩子巩固新学到的数学知识，进一步体会知识的含义和实际应用；另一方面帮助家长指导孩子阅读，体会故事中数学之外的道理，逐步提升孩子的阅读理解能力。

我相信孩子读过这套书后一定会明白，原来，数学不是烦恼，不是包袱，数学真能帮大忙！

奥斯卡在吃他最喜欢吃的午餐——冻比萨饼，这也是他的小狗鲍勃最喜欢吃的。奥斯卡一边吃，一边看一则抽奖的消息。一等奖是 100 个冻比萨饼。奥斯卡看得很兴奋，都忘记把嘴里的食物咽下去了。

"奥斯卡，你没事吧？"妈妈问。

"没事！"奥斯卡说，"我就是想参加这个抽奖！"

奥斯卡的妈妈把抽奖规则读了一遍。"你需要两个汪汪牌狗饼干的盒盖。"妈妈说,"可咱们家里只有一盒。"

转天就是寄出报名表的最后一天了。奥斯卡不知道怎么办才好。

"一边带鲍勃散步,一边想想办法吧。"妈妈说。

　　奥斯卡和小狗鲍勃遇到了艾米和她的大狗纽伯瑞。鲍勃和纽伯瑞相互问好的时候，奥斯卡把抽奖的事告诉了艾米。

　　"我有一个盒盖。"艾米说，"纽伯瑞也吃汪汪牌狗饼干，它的胃口可大呢。"

"要是咱们中奖了，奖品就一人一半。"奥斯卡说，"每人 50 个冻比萨饼！"

　　"那可真是好多好多的比萨饼呀！"艾米说。

　　他们走到艾米家门口，艾米把盒盖剪下来给了奥斯卡。奥斯卡跑回家填好报名表。

100 ÷ 2 = 50

当奥斯卡往邮筒里塞报名表的时候，朋友雨果正好骑车经过。

"你寄什么信呢？"雨果问。

奥斯卡把抽奖的事告诉了他。

"我也想参加。"雨果说，"可是我的推特只吃种子。"推特是雨果养的长尾鹦鹉，它是一只安静的鸟。

雨果回到家。"我还从来没中过奖呢。"他对推特说。

　　推特只是看着他不说话。

三个星期后的一天，一个大盒子出现在了奥斯卡的家门口。他给艾米打电话。

"你猜怎么着？"他说，"咱们中奖啦！"

"是比萨饼吗？"艾米问。

"是棉花糖。"奥斯卡说，"整整 24 包呢。你得 12 包。"

$$24 \div 2 = 12$$

　　"那可真是好多好多的棉花糖呀！"艾米说，"咱
们班去野营的时候，要不要带上呢？"

　　"咱们班一共多少同学？"奥斯卡问。

　　"24个。"艾米回答。

　　"那正好1人1包！"奥斯卡说，"太棒啦！"

$$24 \div 24 = 1$$

那个周末，全班同学围着篝火烤棉花糖。味道很好。可是，只来了 20 个同学，所以还剩下 4 包棉花糖。同学们都很感谢奥斯卡和艾米。

雨果说："你们两个真幸运，我还从来没中过奖呢。"

$$24 \div 20 = 1 \ 余 \ 4$$

过了一个星期，奥斯卡在小镇集市上看到有人卖有奖彩票。一等奖是一台大屏幕电视机。"天哪。"他心想，"要是能在一台大屏幕电视机上看棒球比赛，一定很过瘾！我一定要参加！"

拯救大熊猫
赢巨屏电视机
12元/张

每张彩票 12 块钱。可奥斯卡只有 6 块钱。要是雨果在的话，他们两个就可以每人出 6 块钱。可雨果这个周末出门了。

$$12 \div 2 = 6$$

奥斯卡给艾米打电话。

"6 块钱可不是小数目！"她说，"我们为什么不 3 个人凑彩票钱呢？我出 4 块，你出 4 块，托尼也出 4 块。"托尼是艾米的新邻居。

$$12 \div 3 = 4$$

“我没意见。”奥斯卡说。

“我去跟托尼说，咱们 5 分钟后见！”艾米说。

雨果回家了，奥斯卡把买彩票的事告诉了他。

"要是我也在就好了，我也能凑一份。"雨果说，"我还从来没中过奖呢。"

　　过了两个星期，抽奖的日子到了，他们没有中奖。奥斯卡走到艾米家，把这个消息告诉了她。刚说完，雨果骑着车来了。

　　"你们猜，我得到什么生日礼物了？"他说，"4张棒球赛的门票！我们4个一起去吧！"

奥斯卡、雨果、艾米和托尼看比赛的时候非常开心。每人都有热狗和汽水。托尼带了 12 块泡泡糖，分给大家吃。

12 ÷ 4 = 3

艾米买了一盒爆米花跟大家分享。爆米花盒里还有奖品，是 4 张小小的棒球卡。她也分给每人 1 张。

$$4 \div 4 = 1$$

过了几天，雨果来到奥斯卡的家。"这有个抽奖！"他说，"一等奖是 36 盒泡泡糖。"

"天哪！"奥斯卡说。他看一遍报名表："你想参加吗？"

"嗯……"雨果说，"我在想，或许你和艾米也能跟我一起参加。你们两个总是很幸运。"

　　"可我们上次没有中那台电视机啊！"奥斯卡说。

　　"但你们得过棉花糖呀。"雨果说，"我还从来没中过奖呢。"

　　"好吧。"奥斯卡说，"要是我们赢了，那奖品就分成3份。"

$$36 \div 3 = 12$$

奥斯卡和雨果把抽奖的事告诉了艾米。

"12 盒泡泡糖！"她说，"那可是好多好多的泡泡糖呀！"

"也算我一个吧。"托尼说。

"太棒啦！"雨果说，"要是我们得奖了，就大家一起分。"

$36 \div 4 = 9$

雨果一回到家,就马上填写了报名表。

"你觉得我能转运吗?"他问推特。
推特啄了他几下。

过了一个月，雨果收到一封信，信上说他中了二等奖——一张价值 40 块钱的宠物用品商店的礼品券！奥斯卡、艾米和托尼都跑来庆祝。

"我都不敢相信！"雨果说，"真中奖了！比泡泡糖还好呢！是整整 40 块钱！"

"那可是好多好多的钱呀！"艾米说。

"40 块钱怎么分成 4 份呢？"奥斯卡问。

别人还没算出来时，雨果已经脱口而出："每人 10 块钱！"

"太棒啦！"托尼说，"这下我有钱给小猫买个新窝了。"

他们来到宠物用品商店时，艾米说："我打算看看咬咬胶。"

"鲍勃也能用咬咬胶。"奥斯卡说，"我和你一起去。"

托尼走向宠物猫用品区，雨果直奔宠物鸟专区。

宠物鱼用品

宠物狗用品

宠物鸟用品

过了几分钟,雨果回来了。

"盒子里装的什么?"艾米问。

雨果把盒子打开了,为了能让大家看到盒子里面的东西。"吱吱!"原来是一只艳蓝色的长尾鹦鹉。

"我给推特找了个伴!"雨果说,"你们觉得推特会喜欢它吗?"

"所有的礼物中我觉得推特得到的礼物是最棒的!"奥斯卡说。

你们猜怎么着？推特也是这么想的！

除　　法

这里是几种学习除法的方法：

1. 演示法

 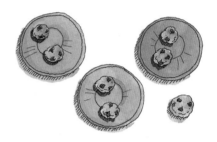

6 块饼干，分成数量相同的 3 份，6÷3=2，每份有 2 块。

7 块饼干，分成数量相同的 3 份，7÷3=2，每份 2 块，还余 1 块。

2. 用乘法表　21÷7=3

我知道 3×7=21，所以 21÷7=3。

练一练：

5÷5=　　　18÷3=

10÷5=　　19÷3=

20÷5=　　20÷3=

40÷5=　　21÷3=

互动课堂

亲爱的家长朋友，请您和孩子一起完成下面这些内容，会有更大的收获哟！

提高阅读能力

- 阅读封面，包括书名等内容。和孩子聊聊，"每人都有份"是什么意思？假如大奖只有一个，怎样能使好几个人同时都得奖呢？

- 请和孩子一起了解以下概念的含义：一人一半，每人一份，一分为三，一分为四。请孩子自己造句子，用到以上的概念。

- 鼓励孩子大声读出书中出现的算式。比如：100 除以 2 等于 50。

- 读过故事以后，请孩子说说，为什么故事里的每个孩子都赢得了奖品？奥斯卡、艾米、雨果、托尼、奥斯卡的小狗鲍勃、艾米的大狗纽伯瑞、鹦鹉推特，艾米的全班同学都得到了什么奖品？

巩固数学概念

● 请用第 32 页图中盘子里的饼干,学习余数的概念。为什么有的时候可以整除?有的时候会有余数?请孩子用盘子里的饼干来演示这两个概念。

● 和孩子一起复习乘法的概念,教孩子如何从乘法转换为除法,比如 $2 \times 5 = 10$,所以 $10 \div 2 = 5$,或者 $10 \div 5 = 2$。

● 请孩子留意第 32 页"练一练"的内容。让孩子说出左边四个算式中的除数和被除数有什么规律,右边的四个算式中的除数和被除数又有什么规律。让孩子试着也写一组算式,满足"商"相同的条件。

生活中的数学

● 给孩子准备 36 个数数的教具,比如纽扣、黄豆、曲别针等都可以。让孩子想象一种奖品,比如一些贴纸,然后请孩子用小盘子将这些教具分组,并回答问题。例如,如果 12 张贴纸,一分为二,或者一分为三,一分为四,一组有几张贴纸? 如果把 36 一分为二,或者一分为三,一分为四,一分为六,甚至分成 12 份呢?

● 请孩子选一种可以分份的奖品,比如 12 张电影票。设计一个抽奖游戏,让孩子在纸上画 4 个赢得电影票的小朋友,他们该怎样平均分配呢?会有多余的电影票吗?

游乐场的票价是每人6元。我和伙伴们一共花了48元，那么，小朋友，你知道我们一共有几个人吗？

快乐的游乐场

提示你一下：
求有几个人，就是求48元里面有几个6元，小朋友，你觉得这样算对吗？

动力小火车实在太小了！每次只能坐 2 个人。除了我们 8 个人，还有 6 个人在排队。小朋友，我们这么多人，需要几次才能坐完？

提示你一下：

先算算我们 8 个人，需要坐几次；再算算排队的 6 个人，需要几次坐完；然后……该你说了，小朋友，然后怎么办？

如果是我来算，我会先算一共有多少人，再求出里面有几个 2。

看看我的方法怎么样？小朋友，你更喜欢哪种方法？

欢迎来到美食餐厅

哇!有 16 个人在用餐!小朋友,如果按照 1 个人吃 1 个苹果、1 块巧克力饼、1 根香肠,喝 1 杯咖啡来计算,那么:

一共需要( )盘苹果?

一共需要( )盘巧克力饼?

一共需要( )盘香肠?

一共需要( )杯咖啡?

游乐场的插花大赛

小朋友,如果平均分配的话,你知道每个花瓶里能够插几枝花吗?

迷宫大冲关

小朋友，看看聪明的你能找到几种走法。试试看！

参考答案

互动练习 1 　　48÷6=8(人)

互动练习 2 　　8÷4=2(辆)
　　　　　　　8÷2=4(辆)

互动练习 3 　　方法一:8÷2=4(次)
　　　　　　　　　　6÷2=3(次)
　　　　　　　　　　4+3=7(次)
　　　　　　　方法二:8+6=14(次)
　　　　　　　　　　14÷2=7(次)

互动练习 4 　　8 盘苹果
　　　　　　　2 盘巧克力饼
　　　　　　　4 盘香肠
　　　　　　　16 杯咖啡

互动练习 5 　　12÷3=4(朵)

互动练习 6 　　黄色

互动练习 7

(习题设计:骆　双)

Everybody Wins!

Oscar was eating his favorite lunch, frozen pizza. It was his dog Bob's favorite, too. While he ate, Oscar read about a contest. First prize was 100 frozen pizzas. Oscar got so excited he couldn't swallow.

"Oscar! Are you all right? "asked his mom.

"I'm fine,"he said. "I've just got to enter this contest!"

Oscar's mother read the contest rules. "You need two Peppy Pooch box tops,"she said,"We only have one box."

The deadline for mailing the entry form was the next day. Oscar wondered what to do.

"Take Bob for a walk while you think about it,"said his mother.

Oscar and Bob ran into Emmy and her dog, Newbery. While Bob and Newbery said hello, Oscar told Emmy about the contest.

"I have a box top ,"said Emmy. "Newbery eats Peppy Pooch, too—lots of it."

"We can split the prize if we win,"said Oscar. "That's fifty frozen pizzas each!"

"That's a lot of pizza,"said Emmy.

They walked to Emmy's house and she gave Oscar a box top. He ran home to fill out the entry form.

While Oscar was mailing his entry form, his friend Hugo rode by.

"What are you mailing?" asked Hugo.

Oscar told him about the contest.

"Wish I could enter," said Hugo. "But Tweeter only eats seeds." Tweeter was Hugo's parakeet. It was a quiet bird.

Hugo went home. "I've never won anything," he told Tweeter.

Tweeter just looked at him.

Three weeks later a box appeared on Oscar's porch. He phoned Emmy.

"Guess what?" he said. "We won a prize!"

"Pizza?" asked Emmy.

"Marshmallows," said Oscar. "Twenty-four bags of them. You get twelve."

"That's a lot of marshmallows," said Emmy. "Should we take them to the class camp-out?"

"How many kids in our class?" asked Oscar.

"Twenty-four," said Emmy.

"A bag for each kid," said Oscar. "Excellent!"

That weekend the class roasted marshmallows around the campfire. They were delicious. Only 20 kids came so there were 4 bags left to share. Everyone thanked Oscar and Emmy.

Hugo said, "You two are so lucky. I've never won anything."

A week later at the village fair Oscar saw some people selling raffle tickets. First prize was a giant-screen TV. "Wow," he thought. "It would be so cool to watch baseball on a giant TV! I've just got to enter!"

Each ticket was 12 dollars. Oscar only had 6 dollars. Hugo would have split a ticket with him. But Hugo was away for the weekend.

Oscar called Emmy.

"Six dollars is a lot of money," she said. "Why don't we split the ticket three ways?   I could pay 4 dollars, you could pay 4 dollars, and Tony could pay 4 dollars."Tony was Emmy's new next-door neighbor.

"Fine with me,"said Oscar.

"I'll talk to Tony and meet you in five minutes,"said Emmy.

When Hugo came back home, Oscar told him about the raffle.

"Wish I'd been here. I could have chipped in,"said Hugo. "I've never won anything."

The raffle drawing was two weeks later. They didn't win a prize. Oscar walked over to Emmy's house to tell her. Just as he finished, Hugo rode up.

"Guess what I'm getting for my birthday?"he said. "Four tickets to the baseball game. We can all go together!"

Oscar, Hugo, Emmy, and Tony had a great time at the game. Everybody had hot dogs and soda. Tony brought twelve packs of bubble gum with him. He split them.

Emmy shared a box of caramel corn. The prize inside was four tiny baseball cards. Emmy shared them, too.

A few days later Hugo went over to Oscar's house."There's this contest," he said. "First prize is thirty-six boxes of bubble gum."

"Wow! "said Oscar. He read the entry form. "Are you going to enter? "

"Well..." said Hugo.   "I was thinking—maybe you and Emmy could enter with me. You're both pretty lucky."

"We didn't win the raffle," said Oscar.

"You won marshmallows," said Hugo. "I've never won anything."

"Okay," said Oscar. "If we win we'll split the prize three ways."

Oscar and Hugo told Emmy about the contest.

"Twelve boxes," she said. "That's a lot of bubble gum."

"I'll enter with you," said Tony.

"Great! " said Hugo. "Then we can all share the prize."

As soon as he got home, Hugo filled out the entry form.

"Do you think my luck will change? " Hugo asked Tweeter.

Tweeter pecked him.

A month later Hugo got a letter saying he'd won second prize—a $40 gift certificate to Pet Depot. Oscar, Emmy and Tony came over to celebrate.

"I can't believe it!" said Hugo. "A real prize! And it's better than bubble gum! It's for forty whole dollars! "

"That's a lot of money," said Emmy.

"What's 40 dollars divided four ways?" asked Oscar.

Before anybody else could figure it out, Hugo said, "Ten dollars."

"Perfect," said Tony. "Now I can buy a new cat bed."

When they got to Pet Depot, Emmy said, "I'm going to look at chew toys."

"Bob could use some chew toys," said Oscar. "I'll go with you."

Tony headed for the cat department and Hugo took off for the bird section.

A few minutes later Hugo appeared.

"What's in that box?" asked Emmy.

He opened it so they could see inside. "Cheep!" said a bright blue parakeet.

"A friend for Tweeter," said Hugo. "Think Tweeter will like it?"

"I think Tweeter's getting the best prize of all," said Oscar.

And guess what? Tweeter thought so, too!